STEVE BARLOW ‡ STEVE SKIDMORE

ZOMBIE
HUNTER

D1589609

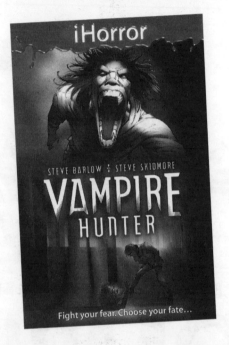

iHorror

ZOMBIE HUNTER

Steve Barlow
&
Steve Skidmore

Illustrated by
Paul Davidson

ORCHARD BOOKS

ORCHARD BOOKS
338 Euston Road, London NW1 3BH
Orchard Books Australia
Level 17/207 Kent St, Sydney, NSW 2000

A Paperback Original
First published in Great Britain in 2011

Text © Steve Barlow and Steve Skidmore 2011
Cover art by Adam Willis © Orchard Books 2011
Inside illustrations and "The 2 Steves" logo
by Paul Davidson © Orchard Books 2011

A CIP catalogue record for this book is available from
the British Library.

ISBN 978 1 40830 986 5

1 3 5 7 9 10 8 6 4 2

Printed in Great Britain

The paper and board used in this paperback are natural recyclable
products made from wood grown in sustainable forests. The
manufacturing processes conform to the environmental regulations of
the country of origin.

Orchard Books is a division of Hachette Children's Books,
an Hachette UK company

www.hachette.co.uk

iHorror

"You better watch out,
unless you want to die."

Victoria Boatwright

iHorror

There is a dark, unseen world around us, of supernatural horrors beyond our imagination. Sometimes the worlds of humans and horrors collide, threatening our very existence.

In iHorror, you make decisions that will affect how the story unfolds. Each section of this book is numbered. At the end of most sections, you will have to make a choice. The choice you make will take you to a different section of the book.

Some of your choices will help you to complete the adventure successfully. But choose wisely. Make the wrong choice and you could end up dead!

Dare you enter the world of iHorror?
Fight your fear. Choose your fate...

Who is the Hunter?

You are the Hunter, protecting the world of humans from supernatural horrors in all their forms. Vampires, werewolves, demons, zombies – you have fought all these creatures and more, and you've always beaten them... so far.

Over more years than you can remember you have become an expert in martial arts, including Jujitsu, Wing Chun and Taekwondo. You have amassed a store of weapons for every occasion: from ancient, magical throwing stars to ultra-modern firearms – including a zombie killer gun that fires highly explosive dumdum shells – whatever it takes to defeat the creatures of the dark, you will use.

Prepare to face your latest test in Zombie Hunter.

And so it begins...

You have been contacted by Mr Romero Price, head of the Nutco Oil Corporation. His company is based on the South Pacific islands of Saruba and Panuka. Saruba is well known to you. For hundreds of years tales from the island have told of the dead rising up out of their freshly dug graves in the form of zombies. But you've never actually been to Saruba. These living dead creatures are difficult to destroy and will not stop hunting for living flesh to feed on.

Mr Price claims that zombies are now highly active on Saruba, which is affecting Nutco's ability to harvest the nut crop grown on the island and process it into oil. As you are the world's expert at dealing with zombies, he has promised to pay you a substantial sum of money to destroy the zombies on the island and to find out where they are coming from. Of course, you have accepted the challenge and are looking forward to once again fighting the creatures of the supernatural.

You have packed the weapons and equipment you think you will need to destroy the zombies, and have flown your private jet to the South Pacific.

There is nowhere to land your jet on Saruba, so you fly to the airport on the neighbouring island of Panuka. Your request for permission to land is granted. But the descent is a bumpy one. Dark storm clouds are gathering as you approach the runway – lightning flashes across the sky and you wonder if this is an omen of what is to come...

‡ *Go to 1.*

1

Heavy rain lashes down as you land your jet and taxi towards the arrivals building. You bring the jet to a halt, power down the engines and open the door. As you descend the steps with your bags, a tall man approaches you, holding out one hand, and carrying a large umbrella in the other. You are surprised to see that, despite the pouring rain, he is wearing sunglasses.

The man introduces himself as a representative of Nutco Oil. "Mr Price has sent me to collect you. He is very anxious to meet you." he says in a strangely slurred and hollow voice. "Nutco's HQ is in the hills of Panuka, so we'll be flying there by helicopter. Please come this way."

He helps to carry your bags to the waiting helicopter through the pouring rain. You stow all of your bags except your case of weapons. You slide this on to the rear seat next to you, put on the helicopter's communication headphones and settle down to enjoy the ride. The man takes his seat in the front and fires up the helicopter's engine.

Soon you are in the air and heading towards the HQ. The weather is getting worse – visibility is limited and lightning crackles across the sky, buffeting the helicopter.

"Do you think we should turn back?" you say to the

1

pilot through your communication mic.

The pilot shakes his head. "Relax – just take it easy. This is going to be the ride of your life – or rather, your death!" He turns round, takes off his glasses and gives you a skull-like grin. Your stomach lurches as you stare into two pus-filled, maggoty eyes – the pilot is a zombie! He laughs manically and thrusts downwards on the controls, sending the helicopter diving towards the ground.

- *If you wish to fight using your martial arts skills, go to 11.*
- *If you wish to use your flame gun, go to 75.*
- *If you wish to shoot the zombie, go to 29.*

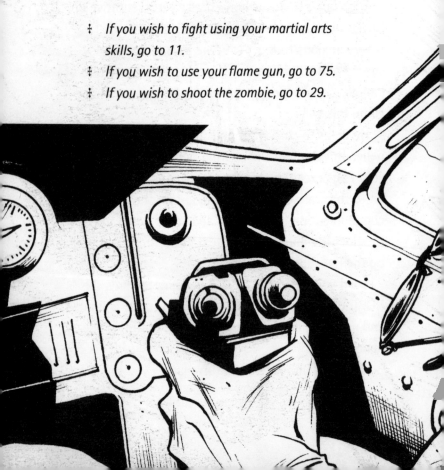

2

Sometime later you wake up and to your surprise, find yourself lying on the wooden deck of a boat. You try to move, but find yourself entangled in a fishing net.

You see the shapes of several fishermen standing above you. They must have pulled you out of the water!

You struggle to get up. "Thank you for..." The words stick in your throat as you stare at the decomposing figures standing above you.

Their hellish faces have evil grins as they take hold of you and begin to tear and rip at your flesh with their deadly teeth. You scream not only in pain but also in the knowledge that you too are about to become a zombie!

‡ *If you wish to start your adventure again, go to 1.*

3

You scramble to your knees, searching for your gun. The zombie brings the club down on your back.

You feel your bones crack and cry out in pain as you fall down. You see the gun in front of you. In desperation, you stretch out your fingertips, but it is just out of reach. Another bone-shattering blow crashes onto your back. Again, you try to reach the gun, but this time it is kicked away by a rotting foot.

Slowly, you turn around and look up into a face from your worst nightmare. You feel another blow and, through dazed eyes, watch helplessly as the zombie kneels over you and opens its mouth to reveal its rotting black teeth. The stench of death is in the air as it plunges its teeth into your body and begins to feed on you. Thankfully, you pass out with the pain.

‡ *Go to 97.*

4

You let the creatures go by. Taking a deep breath, you fling the door open and jump into the corridor.

You take out one of the zombies with a shot to the head. Price and the other zombies turn around in surprise.

"Get down!" you shout at Price as you take down the second zombie. The creature falls to the ground, but its finger is stuck on the trigger of the machine gun. Bullets ricochet off the metal walls. One hits your leg. You curse as you crash against the wall and blood pours from the wound. In that moment, the surviving zombie grabs hold of Price and aims his gun at the executive's heart.

"Don't shoot," begs Price. But looking into his face, you realise he isn't talking to the zombie – he's pleading with you!

‡ *If you wish to do as he says, go to 53.*
‡ *If you wish to try to take the zombie out with a shot, go to 43.*

5

With Price back at his desk, his assistant quietly brings in a pot of fresh coffee, pours out two cups and then promptly leaves.

4
5

"So, what are Nutco using the Kaluta oil for?" you ask Mr Price.

He smiles. "We've discovered that Kaluta oil has incredible properties – it can actually stop the ageing process in humans! We want to use it in beauty products throughout the world. Can you imagine what people would pay for a product guaranteed to stop them looking and getting older? I can! The processed oil is worth a fortune."

You take a sip of the hot coffee. It tastes bitter. "And that's why you want to begin production again?"

"Yes. We have a container ship waiting in Saruba. It was due to be loaded with the oil we've processed already – but the dock workers have fled too. I need your help in stopping this zombie plague. I have a boat at the harbour, waiting to take you over to Saruba. I'll come with you."

You nod. "Then let's get to the harbour. We'll take a car – I'm not sure I want another ride in the helicopter."

While Mr Price orders the car you prepare your weapons. You fit your zombie-killer gun, flamer and extra ammunition onto your customised weapons belt and clip it around your waist.

You head outside, where at last it has stopped raining. You gather your luggage and get into the back seat of a waiting 4x4 with Mr Price.

The drive through the hills to the harbour takes some time. It is dusk as you arrive on the outskirts of the town. The driver of the 4x4 suddenly brakes – you look out and see why – up ahead there is a checkpoint in the road. In the gloom, you can just make out the shapes of a dozen or so figures, signalling the 4x4 to stop.

"Strange," mutters Price, "what's going on here?"

‡ *If you wish to reach for a weapon, go to 80.*
‡ *If you just want to see what happens, go to 49.*

6

You take out the bottle of Kaluta oil and flick the approaching zombies with droplets of oil. The zombies hit with the oil start to smoke and leech black ooze.

They tear at their festering flesh, but the oil is already working, and sending them back to the grave. Some of the other zombies flip over tables and duck down behind them. Others move back, so that they can't be splashed easily with the Kaluta oil. You realise that this is not going to keep them back for very long. You eye up the situation – there are zombies standing at the doorway, holding machetes, but you have the weapons with you to make a fight of it.

‡ *If you want to get out of the café, go to 40.*
‡ *If you want to use your flamer, go to 45.*
‡ *If you want to use your gun, go to 55.*

7

You pick yourself up and run. Avoiding the zombies' clawing hands, you leap through the window. The glass shatters, cutting your hands and face. Arms flailing, you fall through the air and realise that you are two storeys up. You hit the ground with a bone-shattering thump. Through dazed eyes you look up and see a group of misshapen figures lumbering towards you. Then you pass out.

‡ *Go to 97.*

8

Your zombie-killer gun is still empty, so you quickly grab one of the zombies' sub-machine-guns from the floor. You fire a burst at Price, aiming at his head. To your amazement the stream of bullets passes through his head, but doesn't kill him.

01:20

"You've met your match, Hunter," Price rasps, still moving towards you.

‡ *If you want to reload your zombie-killer gun, go to 78.*
‡ *If you want to shoot at another part of Price, go to 58.*

9

You pick up your weapon and jump on to one of the zombie's Harley-Davidson motorbikes. You start it up and, leaving the burning shack, head towards the port.

Your journey to the port doesn't take long. You arrive at the entrance to the docks. You can see some lights and the dark shape of the *Golgotha* is just visible, but you can't use your night-vision binoculars because of the mist. You don't know how the ship is being guarded – or how many zombies there are. You wonder what to do.

‡ *If you want to head to the ship on foot, go to 27.*
‡ *If you want to stay on the motorbike, go to 93.*

10

"Let's get to the island," you say. Manu nods and you head outside to his truck.

The sea mist has long since cleared and you soon arrive at the quay and head for Manu's fishing boat tied up at one of the piers. There is a stiff breeze blowing, and you look at the sky where dark clouds are heading your way.

"We'd better hurry," you tell Manu.

"Yes," he says. "We don't want to get stuck in the bay if the storm hits. It will take almost a day to reach

Saruba, so I've brought some supplies."

You carry your bag to the boat and load on the supplies. Manu fires up the engine and steers away from the pier, heading to Saruba.

Ten minutes later, both your fears are realised as you catch the edge of the passing tropical storm. Waves crash over the boat, tossing it around like a child's toy. Spray stings your face as you struggle through the churning water.

‡ *If you want to head back to Panuka, go to 85.*
‡ *If you want to carry on to Saruba, go to 81.*

11

You lunge forward and grab the zombie in a headlock. He is incredibly strong, but you are stronger. Summoning all your power you twist its head, and with a loud crack the creature's neck breaks. Its face spins around – now it is staring at you while its body remains facing forward! It laughs and snaps at you with its yellow teeth as its hands remain on the controls, forcing the helicopter towards the ground. Time is running out!

‡ *To use the flamer, go to 75.*
‡ *To shoot the zombie, go to 29.*

12

"I will: but only if you tell me what this is all about," you say.

Price makes an angry gesture. "I don't have time for this."

You tap your gun. "I can get a shot at you. I know that if I do, I won't be able to take out all of your zombies before they get me, but you'll still be dead..."

Price considers. "Very well. It's quite simple – I am going to create a world full of zombies!"

You look puzzled. "How?"

"I told you back at the Nutco HQ – I'm using the Kaluta oil in beauty products. I've isolated the virus that creates zombie, and mixed it with the oil. The infected oil will be made into beauty products around the world. When people use such products, the oil and virus will soak into their skin and then into their bloodstream! The virus will turn them into zombies! So much quicker and more effective than just biting someone, don't you think?"

"Why do you need the Kaluta oil?" you ask. "Why not just mix the virus into the beauty products?"

Price smiles. "That's the clever part. Zombies fear Kaluta oil because they know the smoke and flame of burning oil will destroy them. It also harms them in liquid form, but a low dose makes them mindless slaves, obedient to anyone who has the will to be

12

their master. The islanders merely use the oil to force the undead to stay in their graves and not trouble the world of the living. Fools! They have no ambition. If the Kaluta oil is inside the zombies – I will control them! They will have to do as I say – I shall create an army of the undead, obedient only to me!"

"Just one final question and then I'll put down my gun," you say. "Why did you bring me here?"

"You have a great reputation for dealing with supernatural creatures. Only your skills stand in the way of my plans for world domination. You have managed to survive my zombies' attacks so far: but no longer! You will become just another of my slaves... So put down your gun, or I will order my zombies to kill you..."

‡ *If you want to do as Price says, go to 53.*
‡ *If you want to fight the zombies, go to 33.*

13

You kick out at the zombie, taking its legs away from under it. The creature crashes to the floor with an almighty thump and drops the baseball bat. You grab the bat and bring it down onto the zombie's head with a sickening squelch.

The zombie is dead – this time he won't be back.

Your hand aches from the blow you received, but you don't think it's broken. You wonder what you should do next.

‡ *If you want to get into the 4x4, find a hotel and rest, go to 98.*

‡ *If you want to head to Saruba now, go to 65.*

14

You head away from the port around a headland. You use your night-vision binoculars to scan for somewhere to land and find a sandy beach. Through the thickening mist you can just make out a ramshackle beach café. There are motorbikes parked outside the shack. You wade cautiously ashore with your weapon bag and head for the café.

‡ *If you want to take one of the motorbikes, go to 76.*

‡ *If you want to go into the café, go to 23.*

13
14

15

You leap back into the 4x4, slam your foot on the accelerator and speed away, leaving Price to his zombie captors. One of the zombies clings onto the door, clutching at your leg, but you turn the wheel, forcing the 4x4 into a series of tight turns which cause the zombie to lose its grip and spin away.

As you drive off, you slot another clip of dumdum bullets into your zombie-killer gun. You head for the airport, determined to get off this zombie-infested island as quickly as you can.

Suddenly, you feel an excruciating pain in your leg. You look down and see the driver's teeth ripping into your flesh! Having been bitten by a zombie, he has become one! The undead creature crunches down on your leg bone and you let out a scream. Trying to ignore the pain, you blast it with a shot to its head. The creature's head explodes and the body lies on the floor of the jeep, twitching.

In horror and pain, you look at your leg and see a large gaping wound. You realise that the zombie's blood has mixed with your own and you are infected. You have a gruesome choice to make.

- *If you decide to cut off your leg, go to 83.*
- *If you wish to do nothing and accept your fate, go to 26.*

15

16

You aim your rocket launcher with the laser sight and fire at the group of zombies. There is massive explosion and some of the zombies are torn apart. Others are tossed into the air like rag dolls. The fireball catches a couple of fuel drums, and they blast more zombies to tatters and rock the ground. A plume of smoke rises into the air. You sling the launcher over your shoulder and twist the throttle on the bike, heading directly towards the gangway to the ship. With your other hand you fire your gun. The shots are deadly and decapitate several more of the living dead.

Avoiding their bullets, you smash through the remaining zombies, finishing off a couple more with shots to their rotting heads.

You drive the motorbike up the metal gangway and onto the large container ship. As you leap off the bike, you look back and see the zombies pursuing you. You wonder where Price might be being held if he is still alive...

‡ *If you want to head through the door towards the ship's bridge, go to 25.*
‡ *If you wish to head through the door towards the ship's cargo hold, go to 37.*

16

17

You step outside the building and unclip your gun. You position yourself so you can see the door of the harbour building.

The mist swirls around as you wait for the man to appear. Sure enough, the door opens and a figure lumbers out. You give a grim smile – you were right to be suspicious. The heavy-footed figure holds a baseball bat in its rotting hands – it's a zombie! Its pus-filled, yellow eyes stare into the white mist. The creature sniffs at the air and spins to face you – it has caught your scent!

It turns and swings the bat at you at the same time as you pull the trigger. The bullet hits the creature in the chest, but the swinging bat catches your hand. You drop your gun. The wounded zombie moves towards you, bat raised.

‡ *If you want to try and find your gun, go to 3.*
‡ *If you want to use your martial arts skills, go to 13.*

18

You tell the terrified Manu to give the engine full throttle, but your craft is no match for the speed of the zombie boats.

Within seconds all three black boats are circling you. Bullets spray around you, shattering glass in the cockpit. Manu tries to duck down and you return fire, taking three zombies out with head shots.

One of the speedboats pulls up alongside, crashing into Manu's boat, and three zombies jump on board. You are knocked off balance, and one zombie grabs Manu and tears at his flesh. He screams wildly, hacking at the zombie with a knife.

18: You take out a zombie with a head shot.

You manage to shoot another zombie as it lunges for you, turning his head to mush. You quickly aim at the next zombie, but it barges into you, and you miss its head, blasting its arm off instead. Its gun clatters to the deck, and the zombie snarls at you – bringing the wooden club in its other hand smashing down on your arm. Your gun spins out of your hand. Another mighty blow sends you sprawling to the deck.

‡ *If you want to try to escape overboard, go to 59.*
‡ *If you want to reach for your gun, go to 3.*
‡ *If you want to fight the creatures using your martial arts skills, go to 96.*

19

You set the helicopter's navigation system for Nutco's HQ. Flying through the storm, you eventually spot the lights of the helipad through the rain and spray. With great relief you land the helicopter safely.

You are met by several armed guards, who seem surprised by your sudden arrival. "The pilot went to pieces on me," you tell them, pointing at the body of the zombie. "Be careful how you handle it though, if you get blood into any open wounds you'll become living dead yourselves. Now, would someone tell me where can I find Mr Price?"

Wide-eyed, the guards lead you through the rain to the main building, and to Mr Price's office. You tell him what happened in the helicopter.

He seems to be shocked. "I can only apologise," he says. "I didn't realise zombies had reached Panuka, and I'm amazed that it has affected my pilot! This is worse than I thought." He stares at you. "Do you still wish to continue with this assignment?" he asks.

‡ *If you want to carry on, go to 67.*
‡ *If you wish to abandon it and return home, go to 54.*

20

You shoot the zombie easily – it doesn't even see the shot that kills it – again. With the last one gone you quickly go over to find Manu.

You kneel down beside him. Manu looks into your eyes. "You know I am going to turn into a creature of the living dead. Please do not let this happen."

"What about Kaluta oil?" you ask. "Will that stop the changing process?"

He shakes his head. "It is too late, my friend. Do what you must..."

‡ *If you want to try and cure Manu, go to 50.*
‡ *If you decide to obey his request, go to 70.*

21

As quietly as you can, you follow the group down the metal corridors. The stench of the zombies is almost overwhelming in the confined space.

They eventually come to a closed door. Price opens it and steps inside with the zombies.

You wait, then move towards the door and look in. You see hundreds of oil barrels stacked in a huge open space – it's the ship's cargo hold – but there is no sign of Price. You move slowly into the hold.

A voice echoes out. "I am glad you made it, Hunter."

Price emerges from behind the rows of barrels, flanked by a dozen grotesque-looking zombies. Several of them are carrying guns, which are pointed at you.

"I'd put your weapons down, if I were you," says Price. "You and I are outnumbered by the living dead! I don't think we have much chance."

You look around and see two more zombies blocking the doorway behind you. Another zombie moves in from the side, pointing a sub-machine-gun. You realise that Price is right – there are too many zombies to fight and defeat.

‡ *If you wish to talk to Price, go to 82.*
‡ *If you want to put down your gun, go to 53.*
‡ *If you want to try and escape through the door, go to 40.*

21

22

Jumping back into the jeep, you see the driver on the floor. You know that having been bitten, his blood has become infected and he will soon turn into a zombie. You throw him out of the jeep through the smashed windscreen. Then you start up the jeep and head into town, crushing the zombie driver as you go.

It is getting dark as you drive into the town. You are surprised to see that there are very few lights on, and even fewer people on the streets.

- ‡ *If you want to head straight for the harbour and get a boat over to Saruba immediately, go to 56.*
- ‡ *If you want to find a hotel, rest for the night and head to Saruba in the daylight, go to 98.*

23

You open the door of the shack and walk in. There are about a dozen customers sitting at tables. They are all dressed in biker's leathers. You head to the counter where a waiter is standing with his back to you.

"I'm looking for a lift into town," you say. "Can anyone help me?"

The waiter turns round. Your blood turns to ice as you stare into its face. It has no eyes, just sockets

with maggots crawling in the cavities. Its face is covered with rotting flesh and buzzing flies. A roar of laughter breaks out and you spin around to see all the customers standing up. They are all Hell's Angel zombies! Some are holding machetes, some are holding baseball bats. They move towards you with one purpose... to dine on your flesh!

- ‡ *If you want to use your flamer, go to 45.*
- ‡ *If you want to use your gun, go to 55.*
- ‡ *If you want to use the Kaluta oil, go to 6.*

23: The Hell's Angel zombies lumber towards you.

24

It's too late! You are crushed by the zombies as the terrible creatures move towards you, groaning and moaning. Their groping hands claw at your tender, fleshy body.

You try and dodge, but it is no use, there are too many of them. They grab hold of your clothes, and in the struggle pull at your arms and legs tearing you limb from limb. You scream in agony before passing quickly into the peace of death.

‡ *If you wish to begin your adventure again, go to 1.*

25

You head through the nearest door and set off along the narrow metal corridors, gun ready. The thudding noise of the huge ship engines is all you can hear. The corridors are poorly lit – strip lights buzz on and off over your head – and despite your experience, your heart pounds in your chest. You know that the zombies realise you are on board and are no doubt hunting for you. Suddenly you can just hear the sound of slow, lumbering footsteps. And they are coming towards you!

‡   *To head towards them, go to 64.*
‡   *To find somewhere to hide, go to 79.*

26

You feel the zombie's infected blood travel through your body, mixing with your own. You pass into unconsciousness.

Sometime later you awaken. Your throat is dry and you feel hungry. But food and water will not do for you – you have a taste for human blood and flesh. You have become one of the living dead – a zombie!

‡   *If you wish to begin your adventure again, go to 1.*

25
26

27

You park up the bike and take your rocket launcher out of its bag. Carefully you move through the mist, listening and watching out for any sign of zombie activity.

You get closer to the ship as you detect a moaning sound – and it's getting closer! In the mist you can't really tell where it's coming from, so you ready yourself for action. At that moment, a dozen or so zombies step out of the mist. They are armed with guns and clubs. The rotting creatures move towards you, moaning with each pace.

‡ *If you want to tell them to take you to Price, go to 68.*
‡ *If you want to use the rocket launcher, go to 84.*
‡ *If you want to use your gun, go to 51.*

28

You sidestep the zombie's attack easily and catch the creature with a snap kick to its head. It falls on its face and you kneel on its shoulders, grabbing a handful of matted hair to force its head back.

"Who sent you?" you say. The zombie continues to struggle.

You pull harder and are shocked to hear a loud crack as the zombie's neck breaks. You let go and watch as the creature's head swings wildly from side to side! The zombie grabs hold of you and lets out a roar. More zombies appear in the lobby, heading towards you.

You manage to struggle free from the zombie's grip and shoot it. However, the other zombies surround you. Before you can turn your gun on them, one of them knocks it from your hand and punches you to the floor. The other zombies move in for the kill...

‡ *If you want to try and escape, go to 40.*
‡ *If you want to fight the zombies, go to 59.*

29

The green jagged hills of the island rush up to meet you with terrifying speed. Lightning bolts criss-cross the cloud-covered sky. Quickly you flick open your weapons case and pull out your zombie-killer gun.

‡ *To shoot the zombie in the head, go to 86.*
‡ *To shoot the zombie in the back, go to 44.*

30

You tuck the gun under your arm and unlock the door. You wait a second before you turn the handle and fling the door open.

Four zombies are standing in the hallway. The stink of the undead creatures is almost overwhelming. Before they can react, you swing the open bottle and shower the zombies with Kaluta oil. They stagger back, trying to wipe the oil from their bodies. Smoke swirls from their rotting skin as black ooze runs out of gashes in their flesh. They wail and moan before collapsing to the carpet in a heap of torn rags and bones.

Standing over the zombies, you notice a piece of torn paper clutched between two bony fingers.

You pick it up and read it.

> To the Hunter
> If you are reading this, you have survived!
> But I have Price. He is still human - for now.
> If you want to see him again, come to the ship,
> Golgotha, in Port Saruba.
> Do not delay!

You wonder who or what is behind this and why you are so wanted...

☩ *Go to 46.*

30

31

The rocket clicks into place and you manage to get another shot off. It shreds a zombie into a million pieces, but the others are still coming. They crash into you, snapping their rotting teeth, and you all slam into the ground. One of the zombies grabs the launcher – and you try to wrestle it from its grip. You can feel teeth biting you all over. Just as you grab the launcher back, the creature pulls the trigger. You only see the flash of white light as the rocket detonates, ripping through you and the zombies around you.

‡ *You have failed. If you are brave enough to begin again, go to 1.*

32

Sometime later, you wake up. Your throat is dry and an empty hunger gnaws at your stomach. You have a taste for human blood and flesh. Your plan did not work! You have become that which you hunted – a zombie!

‡ *If you are brave enough to begin your adventure again, go to 1.*

31
32

33

"Not today," you say. You dive to the floor and roll along the ground, avoiding the zombies' bullets. At the same time you shoot at the barrels of Kaluta oil. Your bullets rip holes in the steel drums and a torrent of Kaluta oil surges onto the zombies and Price. The zombies closest to the shower of oil wail as smoke rises from their decaying bodies. They drop their weapons as they become drenched with oil, and slowly turn to heaps of black ooze and bone.

33: Price and the zombies are engulfed in Kaluta oil.

33

Price screams orders at his zombie horde, but the oil is too powerful – the undead creatures stagger around confused, slipping and falling over. Price dives to pick up a gun, but he is surrounded by the zombies, who move in on him. An overdose of the oil has driven them mad and they take no notice of him as they slash and tear at his flesh. His cries are drowned out by their wailing.

As the pool of virus-contaminated oil grows you take down several zombies with shots to heads, causing a shower of maggots. You aim again and the gun clicks onto an empty chamber – you have run out of ammunition!

‡ *If you want to reload your gun, go to 48.*
‡ *If you wish to set an explosive charge, go to 72.*

34

As the zombies beat at the 4x4, you aim your gun at one of the creatures and shoot. Its head explodes in a shower of shattered bone and black ooze.

The others continue their attack without pausing. As you continue to shoot, one of the zombies climbs onto the bonnet of the 4x4. You spin around and fire. The windscreen shatters, showering you with glass. You look up and see a gaping hole in the zombie's chest, but you have not killed it! Another shot takes its head clean off and the creature drops to the ground.

Zombies punch and kick the doors. The back windows implode as the creatures continue their assault. Zombies clutch at you and Price. You shoot at the zombie that has Price. The zombie's chest explodes and a gaping wound appears. But it isn't dead – its hands grasp tightly around Price's neck and begin to choke him.

"Help me," he wheezes.

You lean over Price and shoot the zombie in the head at point blank range. It releases Price and slumps down dead. You realise that you have to employ a different tactic if you are going to survive this attack.

‡   *If you want to try and drive away, go to 63.*
‡   *If you want to get out of the 4x4 and run away, go to 71.*

34

35

Just as the last zombie leaps from the black speedboat you pull out you flamer. You send a blast of flame towards the zombie and it bursts into flames. Suddenly you realise that you have made a big mistake. The zombie leaps onto the fishing boat and it starts to catch fire. Before you can react, fuel cans on the deck explode. You are thrown up and out of the burning vessel. You hit the water and pass out.

⸸ *Go to 2.*

36

"What were you checking?" you ask the woman.

"That you aren't a creature from the dead," she replies.

"How can you tell I'm not?"

She points at the liquid. "Kaluta oil," she says. "It protects us from the undead creatures. You would have reacted to it, if you were a zombie."

"Powerful stuff," you say.

"Unfortunately, it is needed in these troubled times. You will need some if you are staying here." She passes over a bottle. "I hope you don't have to use it."

"I probably will – I'm going to Saruba tomorrow," you say.

She shakes her head. "Rather you than me. I may be able to help you. I will contact someone I know. His name is Manu. He will be here in the morning."

You thank her and head for your room with your luggage and the Kaluta oil held firmly in your hands.

‡ *Go to 69.*

36: The lady at the desk gives you some Kaluta oil.

37

You head through a door and make your way down the metal corridors and stairs. You know that the zombies realise you are on board and are no doubt hunting for you. A sign points towards the cargo hold. You hear the sound of footsteps ahead of you. They are getting nearer! Your heart pounds and you know you have to make a quick decision.

- *If you want to head back the way you came, go to 88.*
- *If you wish to carry on towards the sound, go to 64.*

38

You turn the helicopter around and head back to the airport. The rain thrashes against the windscreen making it difficult to see, even with the wipers on. Wind gusts at high speed shaking the helicopter.

You struggle with the controls, desperately trying to keep the helicopter in the air, but a bolt of lightning forks across the sky and hits the rotor blades. The engine bursts into flame and all electrical power is lost. The helicopter plummets downwards, spinning wildly out of control. You open the door – and in a desperate attempt to save your life – throw yourself out with a wild cry. You hit the trees and feel your limbs breaking as you plunge to the hard, rocky ground. At the same time, the helicopter hits the ground and explodes; the heat of the fireball burns your skin.

As you lie drifting in and out of consciousness, you sense the presence of someone standing at your feet. You look up and see the rotting face of another zombie. The creature lurches towards you, mouth open. You can smell its stinking, putrid breath as the creature crouches over you and rips at your arm with its teeth. You cry out in agony and pass out.

‡   *Go to 97.*

39

You shoot another stream of fire at the remaining zombies and they burst into flames. The inside of the shack is now an inferno! The walls and the ceiling are ablaze and the zombies who are still moving crash about, roaring as they try to put out the fire that is slowly destroying them.

You move towards the door, but as you do a zombie crashes into you and grabs hold of you. Your clothes burst into flames as the creature holds on to you. You try to break free but can't. More zombies grab hold of you. The smell of burning flesh fills the air. You scream in pain as the last sight you see is the burning, charred faces of the zombies before you pass into blackness.

꙳ *You have failed. If you are brave enough to begin again, go to 1.*

40

You rush towards the doorway, punching at the two zombies who are blocking your way. You manage to land some good hits, but cannot force your way through.

You feel your neck being grabbed from behind. You try to spin around, but more powerful hands grab at your body and your arms are pinned to your side.

39
40

A zombie moves towards you, its skin is covered in sores and maggots crawling in its seeping wounds. Its blackened mouth opens, revealing its misshapen teeth. "No!" you cry, but you are helpless. The creature rips at your neck. He is soon joined by the others as they feed on what they crave – human flesh!

⸸ *Go to 26.*

41

You shake your head sadly. "Sorry, you're a goner," you say.

You turn and are instantly knocked backwards as a zombie smashes you across the face with a wooden club. All your attention had been on Price and you hadn't seen the creature coming for you from behind!

You fall to the ground and drop your gun. Blood gushes from your head and through dazed eyes you watch the zombie pick up the gun and crush it with its hand. The other zombies wail and moan loudly.

You try to get to your feet, but you can only lie there completely dazed as you hear the other zombies closing in on you.

⸸ *Go to 96.*

42

"Time to put you back in the ground," you say before pulling the trigger. The shot severs the zombie's head and it bounces to the floor as the body crashes down next to it. You pick up the bottle Eric was holding and examine the contents. "Coloured water," you murmur. "These Zombies are getting smart."

At that moment another man walks into the lobby. He stares wide-eyed at the dead zombie on the floor.

"What happened here?" the man asks.

"Oh, we had an argument and he lost his head." You point your gun at the man.

"Whoa! Wait a minute. I'm Manu – I've come to collect you."

"Care to prove it?"

"I've got this." He produces a bottle of Kaluta oil.

"We'll use mine." You take out your bottle of oil and flick some oil at Manu. Nothing happens. You hold out a hand.

"Glad to meet you."

‡ *If you want to find out more about Manu, go to 52.*

‡ *If you want to get over to Saruba immediately, go to 10.*

43

You shake your head and aim your gun. "I can get it..." you mutter. But before you can pull the trigger, the zombie pushes Price towards you. The executive staggers into you and you crash to the floor.

The zombie leaps across the floor and grabs hold of you and plunges his teeth into your shoulder, ripping off a chunk of your flesh. You scream in agony, but at the same time manage to get a shot at the zombie's head. It explodes, but you know you are fatally wounded.

‡   *Go to 26.*

44

You pull the trigger. Bullets rip through the seat and explode in the zombie's body, spraying pus across the windscreen. The creature slumps forward and you lean over to grab hold of the controls.

As you do, a powerful hand grabs your throat – despite having a huge hole in its chest you haven't destroyed the zombie! You smash your fist into its maggoty face and manage to twist out of its deadly grip. The creature laughs and, grabbing the controls again with both hands, sends the helicopter into another death spin.

‡ *If you want to shoot the zombie in the head, go to 86.*
‡ *If you wish to use your flamer, go to 75.*

45

With lightning reactions, you unclip the flamer from your belt and release a sheet of fire at the Hell's Angel zombies. Several burst into flames and two are turned to ashes immediately by the intensity of the heat. The burning zombies stagger about, stumbling into each other and setting fire to their undead companions.

You fire another jet of flame, torching several more creatures. The wooden shack catches alight and begins to burn.

‡ *If you want to get out of the building now, go to 62.*
‡ *If you wish to finish off the remaining zombies, go to 39.*

45

46

You manage to catch a few hours' rest and just as dawn is breaking you gather your weapons together: your trusted zombie-killer gun and your flamer. You also have two powerful explosive charges with a timer. You reload your guns and snap them into place on your belt, along with the explosives. You also pull out your long-range rocket launcher. It has laser sights and five rockets that explode on impact. You slide it into a bag and sling it over your shoulder before heading down to reception.

The woman from last night isn't behind the desk, but there is a man sitting in the lobby. "I'm Eric," he says, "I'm supposed to be meeting you..."

Although he doesn't look like your average zombie, you decide to make sure. "I had a bad night's sleep and I'm feeling a little jumpy. Prove you're human and not a zombie..."

Eric smiles and takes out a bottle of Kaluta oil. He opens it and splashes his face with it. "OK?" he smiles.

‡ *If you trust Eric, go to 90.*
‡ *If you want more proof, go to 99.*

47

Before the zombies can react, you roll across the ground, at the same time reaching for your flamer. In one movement you pull it out, aim it at the first zombie and unleash a jet of fire at the creature. It bursts into flames and wails as it staggers about, stumbling into another zombie and setting its clothes alight too.

Another jet of flame causes two zombies to explode.

"Price!" you shout. "Price!" But he has disappeared. There is no sign or sight of him. You send another sheet of flame at the group of zombies, and they duck down behind the 4x4.

‡ *If you want to look for Price, go to 77.*
‡ *If you wish to get out of here, go to 15.*

48

You reload your gun as the zombies continue to tear at Price. At that moment you are grabbed from behind. You had forgotten about the zombies at the doorway – they are not covered in the oil!

You slam one in the face with an elbow strike – knocking its jaw clean off. Flies buzz out of the zombie's mouth and into your face. You drop your

47
48

shoulder down, flinging the zombie over your head and onto the floor in front of you. Quickly, you unsling your rocket launcher and just as the zombie gets up you swing the launcher round and smash off its head. But the remaining zombie leaps on your back and twists your head with a powerful jerk. Your neck snaps loudly and you drop to the floor.

‡ *Go to 32.*

49

As the 4x4 stops, you look out of the window and your blood turns cold. Moving towards the vehicle is a group of zombies! Their skin is rotting and several of them have open wounds which ooze black liquid. Their yellowing eyes stare at you in hatred. Before you can react a fist smashes through the window, shattering the glass. A claw-like hand grabs hold of the driver's head, twists it and pulls it off! Blood fountains out, splattering the jeep windscreen and interior red. Price cries out in fear as you reach for your zombie-killer gun.

The door next to you is wrenched off and one of the creatures catches hold of your arm, knocking your gun to the floor. You smash frantically at it with your fist, but cannot break free – desperately you try and reach for your other weapons, but you cannot get hold of them. You are dragged from the vehicle into the horde of undead creatures.

‡ *If you wish to try and run away from the zombies, go to 24.*

‡ *If you want to try and fight them, go to 59.*

49: The windscreen is splattered with blood.

50

You shake your head. "If I find who is behind the rise of the zombies, they might be able to help you. Until then, I'll make sure you don't do anyone any harm."

Despite Manu's protests, you patch up his wounds, making sure you don't get any infected blood on you, before dragging him to the back of the boat and tying him up with a rope. Then you fire up the boat's engine and head towards Saruba.

Half an hour later you are nearing the island. "Nearly there," you say. You turn and are going to smile at Manu. You gasp in shock – he has broken free and is standing behind you – his eyes are blank. He has turned into a zombie! The creature steps towards you, grabs your throat and slowly squeezes your windpipe, cutting off your breath. You are powerless to fight back against this supernatural strength. His teeth rip into your cheek and tear off a lump of flesh. You pass out in agony.

✣ *Go to 32.*

51

You open fire with your zombie-killer gun and take out three of the creatures. The zombies with guns shoot back. To avoid their bullets, you dive behind some wooden crates and continue firing.

The creatures get nearer and their shots riddle the crates. Suddenly a zombie leaps over the top of the crate. You take it out with a single shot, but it lands on top of you, knocking your gun out of your hand and trapping you on the ground. More zombies surround you. You struggle to get up, but are helpless as they move in for the kill.

‡ *Go to 96.*

52

You ask Manu to tell you more about himself. He explains he is a local fisherman and has family on Saruba. They have been scared by the number of zombies that are now on the island and are in hiding. He has a boat and can take you to the island.

"Do you know why so many zombies are on Saruba?" you ask.

Manu tells you that when the Nutco Corporation took over the island's export trade of Kaluta oil, they stopped the local people from using it for purification purposes, because they wanted all of the oil.

"What do you mean?" you ask.

He tells you that Kaluta oil is poured onto graves to stop the undead from arising. Now, because Nutco have stopped this, zombies are all over the island.

"Is there anything else that the oil does?" you enquire.

Manu nods. "Burning the oil produces thick smoke that kills zombies. This was how my people on Saruba could get rid of any zombie that awoke..."

You are still puzzled about who is behind the kidnapping of Price, but you thank Manu for his information.

‡ *Go to 10.*

53

You nod "OK" and lower your gun. At once you realise it is a mistake as the zombies pull the triggers on their guns.

Bullets rip into your body, sending you crashing to the floor. As you lie helpless and bleeding, a zombie bends over you and rips at your flesh with its teeth – grateful for this unexpected treat. You scream in agony before the pain causes your body to shut down.

‡ *Go to 97.*

54

You think carefully – if zombies have reached Panuka, it probably means they have spread too far for you to stop them. "I think I'll be heading home," you reply.

Mr Price gives you a scornful look. "I thought you were supposed to be fearless."

"I'm also very careful – that's why I'm still alive," you say.

He is disgusted with you. "Well, you're obviously not the person I was told you were. I'll get a driver to take you back to the airport."

You head outside, gather your luggage and get into the back seat of a waiting 4x4. "Take me to the airport," you tell the driver.

53
54

Some miles down the road, you come to a roadblock. It is manned by several figures. They stop the car and yank open the door.

"What the..." The words stick in your throat as you stare up into the face of a zombie. Its head tilts to the side and its tongue sticks out, dripping with spit and blood. Before you can react, the creature grabs hold of you and with inhuman strength drags you out of the car and throws you on the ground. You look up and realise that the other figures are also zombies!

‡ *If you wish to fight using your martial arts skills, go to 96.*

‡ *If you want to try and reach the 4x4 for your gun, go to 24.*

55

You reach for your gun and start shooting at the creatures of the living dead. Your aim is good and three of the zombies fall to the ground, their brains taken out by the explosive bullets.

You keep shooting, but there are too many of the creatures to deal with all at once. You feel a blow to the back of your head and you drop to the ground, stunned. You look up to see the zombies closing in...

- ‡ *If you want to use your martial arts skills, go to 59.*
- ‡ *If you want to use your flamer, go to 45.*
- ‡ *If you want to try and get out of the café, go to 40.*

56

You drive through the town to the harbour and park the 4x4. A sea mist has come down, and visibility is poor. Grabbing your luggage, you make your way to the harbour office. The air itself seems to cling to you. Somewhere in the distance a foghorn blasts a warning.

There is a light on inside the wooden building, so you push the door open. A man sits behind the counter watching a television. He has his back to you.

"I need to get over Saruba, straight away," you

say. "Can I hire a boat and someone to take me over? Money is no problem..."

The man doesn't turn around. "I'll do it. Pier three," he replies in a toneless voice. "Wait for me there. I'll be with you in a minute..."

✢ *If you want to head to pier three, go to 73.*
✢ *If you are suspicious of the man, go to 17.*

57

You run for the door, but Price is too quick. He catches hold of you and knocks you to the oil-covered floor. Your gun spins from your hand. You try and fight him off using your martial arts skills, but he is too strong for you.

1:00

His teeth sink into your flesh time and time again. You feel the mixture of infected zombie blood and Kaluta oil pulsing through your veins. It seems to give you a greater strength. You manage to break free of Price's grip and begin to attack him. The two of you punch and kick at each other.

0:30

Suddenly you stop fighting, allowing Price to grab you in a headlock. "You are going to become one of the living dead," says Price, baring his teeth. "I win, Hunter."

0:20

You laugh. "There's no winner here... Time's up..." You point at the explosives. "We're both dead men."

0:10

Price realises what is about to happen and rushes towards the device. He is too slow. The explosive charges detonate, setting off a chain reaction as the thousands of gallons of oil catches alight. You are hit with a wall of heat and power as the whole ship explodes in a massive fireball.

‡ *You have stopped Price, but you have paid with your life. If you wish to start again, go back to 1.*

58

"I don't think so," you reply. You aim the sub-machine-gun at Price's legs and open fire. The bullets rip through the bulging muscle and shatter bone, sending Price tumbling to the floor.

01:10

He flails around, trying desperately to claw his way forward and reach you.

‡ *Go to 100.*

58

59

You scramble to your feet, kicking out at the creatures as they move in for the kill.

One of the zombies steps in front of you, grabs hold of your neck and squeezes hard. Your windpipe is slowly being crushed. In a final effort to save yourself, you punch the zombie in the face.

To your amazement your fist passes through its rotting, pus-filled head. You can feel its brain slithering under your fingers. You take hold of it and pull with all your might. The brain comes away from the skull, causing the creature to release its grip on you as it drops down dead.

You throw the brain on the floor and face the other zombies, who move towards you with one purpose in mind – to feast on your flesh!

‡ *Go to 96.*

59: The zombie's brain wriggles with maggots.

59

60

You jump off the bike, kneel down, aim and launch a rocket at the oncoming zombies. They are ripped apart by the explosion, but through the smoke and mist you can see that more are still coming.

‡ *If you want to continue to use the rocket launcher, go to 31.*
‡ *If you want to use your gun, go to 51.*
‡ *If you want to sneak round to the service gangway, go to 66.*

61

"Give me a moment," you say as you pick up the oil and your gun and move towards the door.

You can hear heavy breathing coming from out in the corridor. You realise that you can't open the door and hold the bottle and your gun at the same time.

    ‡ *If you wish to keep hold of the bottle of Kaluta oil, go to 30.*

    ‡ *If you wish to keep hold of your gun, go to 87.*

62

Blasting further jets of flame, you clear a pathway to the door. You rush out of the burning building into the cool, white mist outside. As you hurry away from the blazing inferno, the roof collapses and a ball of fire erupts, knocking you to the ground and sending your flamer spinning away from you. Dazed, you pick yourself up off the ground.

    ‡ *If you want to kill off any surviving zombies, go to 65.*

    ‡ *If you want to head to the port, go to 9.*

63

You climb over the front seat, push the body of the driver out of the way and restart the engine.

As you do so, the front door of the 4x4 is ripped off and a zombie grabs hold of your arm and starts to tug at it. It feels as though your arm is being pulled out of its socket! You know that you have to destroy a zombie's brain if you wish to kill it, so you point your gun into the creature's face and fire. The zombie's head explodes and it drops down dead.

At the same time one of the back doors is ripped off and a powerful zombie grabs Price.

"No!" he screams as the zombie pulls him from the vehicle. You jump out and point your gun, but realise that if you shoot the zombie, the dumdum bullets may injure Price as well.

‡ *If you want to escape and leave Price to his fate, go to 15.*
‡ *If you wish to try and rescue Price, go to 89.*

64

You continue along the corridor. From out of the gloom, you see three zombies armed with sub-machine-guns. Price is walking in front of them.

He sees you.

"Hunter!" he cries out. The zombies raise their weapons. You immediately shoot one of the zombie captors in the head.

Price shrieks in terror.

The other two begin shooting and you throw open a metal door and use it to partly shield yourself, still firing...

Another zombie drops to the floor, but the other grabs hold of Price and opens his mouth, ready to bite at the captured executive's neck.

"Don't shoot," pleads Price.

You step out from behind the door.

‡ *If you wish to do as he says, go to 53.*
‡ *If you wish to try to take the zombie out with a head shot, go to 43.*

65

As you go to pick up your weapon, an old granny holding a shotgun steps out of the white mist. She points it at you, "You killed my boy!" You see that her face is made up of rotting flesh and open wounds. It is another zombie!

You snatch your flamer up, but as you take aim the zombie granny fires her shotgun. You stagger backwards, and a jet of fire from your flamer arcs into the night sky as the shot hits you in the chest. You look up to see the zombie granny engulfed in flames. You drop to your knees, your lifeblood pumping out of your body. You try to crawl away and find help, but the effort is too much. The mist covers you like a shroud as you pass into blackness.

‡ *You have paid the ultimate price. If you wish to begin your adventure again, go back to 1.*

65

66

In the confusion you sneak round behind some crates. Using the cover of the smoke and mist you reach the service gangway. But you've been spotted! Zombies chase you up the ramp to the ship – some shooting towards you as they run. You dodge between some more crates and spot a door.

⸸ *If you want to run for the doorway, go to 37.*
⸸ *If you want to stop and shoot the zombies, go to 51.*

65: The zombie granny aims her shotgun at you.

66

67

"I'm not going to let a little fight with a zombie put me off," you tell Price. "Tell me what's happening around here."

Mr Price confirms that zombies are running loose on Saruba, where Nutco have a processing plant. The zombies have scared the plant's workers away, causing oil production to shut down. The island's inhabitants have barricaded themselves in their homes for fear of a zombie attack. No amount of persuasion, or money, can get the workers back to the factory.

"What are you processing?" you ask.

"Kaluta nuts," replies Price. "We're turning them into oil – oh, but where are my manners. Please take a seat and I will have some coffee sent up." You sit down on an expensive-looking sofa while Mr Price steps into the adjoining room.

You vaguely remember something you read about Kaluta nuts.

‡ *If you want to quickly research some information about the Kaluta nut, go to 92.*

‡ *If you want to wait for Mr Price to continue his story, go to 5.*

68

You hold up your hands. "Take me to your leader, or take me to where Price is being held."

The zombies leer and laugh. One of them shoots at you. You are hit in the leg and you cry out as you feel bone shatter. Blood seeps through your trousers and down your thigh. The zombies howl and lick their lips at the smell of fresh blood. They don't want to kill you yet though – they want fresh meat. You realise that you were stupid to try and negotiate with a bunch of zombies.

- ⁑ *If you want to use the rocket launcher, go to 84.*
- ⁑ *If you want to use your gun, go to 51.*

69

You climb up two flights of stairs, find your room and collapse on the bed for a well-earned rest. You soon drift into an uneasy sleep, but some time later you are awoken by a persistent knocking on the door. You switch on the bedside lamp.

"Who is it?" you ask.

A deep-throated voice replies, "Room service."

‡ *If you have some Kaluta oil, go to 61.*
‡ *If you don't have any Kaluta oil, go to 94.*

70

You know that Manu is right – he doesn't want to become a zombie.

You shake his hand, say goodbye and promise to look after his family on Saruba when the zombie curse is ended. You go over to the cockpit and grab a bottle of Kaluta oil, when you hear a snarling noise behind you. Quickly you turn round – Manu has gone zombie! Saliva dribbles from his mouth, his eyes have turned yellow and he is clawing at the deck of the boat with his fingernails.

"Oh, Manu," you sigh, but you know Manu is dead already.

69
70

The zombie pounces at you. In one swift movement you grab your gun and duck down. It flies over you. You blast it in the head and the zombie body splashes down into the water.

All you can do now is set course for Saruba, with your promise to Manu to be kept.

By the time you arrive at the island the sun is fading from the sky as night approaches. You see a large container ship with lights on in the port – you realise that this must be the *Golgotha*, the ship where Price is being held. Using your powerful night-vision binoculars you check out the dockside. You soon realise that the place is crawling with zombies! Some have guns and seem to be guarding the ship.

‡ *If you want to cruise into the port, go to 95.*
‡ *If you want to find somewhere else to land, go to 14.*

71

Shooting at the zombies, you throw open the door and grab Price – who seems to be in shock.

"Come on!" you yell at Price. He follows you as a zombie grabs your arm. You manage to twist out of its grasp and shoot at it. The zombie's arm explodes at the shoulder, but it clutches at you with its other hand. Another zombie grabs you from behind, but before it can sink its teeth into your flesh, you send it flying over your shoulder with a perfect judo throw – knocking the other zombie backwards. You crush its spongy skull under your boot.

At that moment, Price stumbles to the floor. He is immediately surrounded by a group of six or seven zombies, all frothing black ooze from their mouths.

"Help me!" Price pleads. The zombies reach down and take hold of the struggling executive.

‡ *If you want to try and rescue Mr Price, go to 89.*
‡ *If you decide that you should leave him and save yourself, go to 41.*

72

You leave Price to his fate and reach down to your weapons belt. You unclip a small explosive charge

71
72

and attach it to the metal wall of the cargo hold. You punch the buttons and set the timer for two minutes.

02:00

As you move towards the door, you are stopped in your tracks by a roar of supernatural rage that fills the hold and zombie bodies are flung into the air. You are forced to duck out of the way as body parts rain down. You turn and see Price rising to his feet in the midst of his former slaves.

72: Body parts fly through the air.

It is a nightmarish vision – his flesh is ripped from his body – an eyeball hangs out of his socket, his muscles and tendons hang loosely, exposed by the zombies' attack. But the combination of highly concentrated oil and virus acting on living flesh has turned Price into a super-zombie!

01:30

With incredible speed and strength, he attacks the zombies, smashing their skulls with a series of punches and kicks. He then heads towards you...

‡ *If you wish to stop Price escaping, go to 8.*
‡ *If you want to get out of the hold, go to 57.*

73

You leave the building and make your way cautiously through the thickening sea mist to pier three. You stand waiting for the man, listening to the lapping of the waves against the harbour wall and the wail of a foghorn somewhere out in the gloom. It is not long before you hear a creak, and the sound of heavy footsteps on the wooden boards of the pier. The footsteps stop. You can't see anything through the thick mist. You unclip your gun and step forward, ears and eyes straining for some sign of life.

THWACK!

From out of the mist a wooden club rushes down towards your head. With your lightning reflexes you just manage to block it with your hand. But your gun is knocked to the ground and spins away from you across the wooden planks. A zombie quickly lurches from the white shroud-like mist, its face is covered in torn, pus-filled holes and seaping blisters. It raises the wooden baseball bat again.

‡   *If you want to try and find your gun, go to 3.*
‡   *If you want to use your martial arts skills,
     go to 13.*

73

74

You reach into your weapon bag and take out your rocket launcher. You use the laser sight to aim at one of the zombie speedboats and pull the trigger. The rocket blasts toward the boat, trailing a tail of smoke. The zombies don't know what hit them. The boat explodes in a ball of flame, flinging zombie parts in the air. You aim at the second speedboat and fire another shot. This time the zombies try to dive overboard, but the rocket is too powerful, and they disappear in a flash of orange. The third boat is too close. It crashes into Manu's fishing boat and you stagger to keep your balance. Three zombies jump aboard.

Quickly, you reach for your zombie-killer gun and take out two of the undead creatures with well-aimed shots. At that moment you hear Manu scream in agony. You spin around and see the third zombie ripping at the poor man's throat. Manu fights back with his fishing knife, hacking at the zombie's neck. The last zombie on the black speedboat opens fire, forcing you to quickly duck out of the way. You see Manu slice the zombie's head off before he crashes to the deck.

‡ *If you decide to shoot the last zombie, go to 20.*
‡ *If you want to use your flamer, go to 35.*

75

As the helicopter plummets towards the ground, you flick open your weapons case and pull out your flamer. You blast the zombie with a jet of fire. The creature is engulfed by swirling orange flames and screams as it thrashes about, its rotting flesh shrivelling in the heat.

However, you quickly realise that you have made a big mistake – the helicopter is now on fire – smoke filling the cockpit – and it is still diving towards the ground. You desperately try to reach past the blazing zombie for the controls, but your situation is hopeless. Your clothes catch fire and as you try to beat out the flames, the helicopter smashes into the ground.

‡ *Go to 97.*

76: A zombie swings his gruesome baseball bat at you.

75

76

You take out your gun and head to one of the Harley-Davidsons parked outside the shack. You jump astride it and try the kick start several times, but the engine won't fire. Then from out of the mist a figure appears. It is dressed in biker's leathers and is holding a baseball bat.

"Get off my ride!" it growls.

You stare at its matted hair and rotting flesh, and realise you are facing a zombie Hell's Angel! Before you can react, it swings the club against your head. You are knocked from the bike and your gun flies from your hand. The zombie stands over you, club raised.

‡ *If you want to try and reach your gun, go to 3.*

‡ *If you wish to use your martial arts skills, go to 91.*

77

The zombies you have set alight stagger around while the others hide. "Price!" you shout. "Where are you?" There is no reply. Keeping a wary eye on the remaining zombies, you reload your zombie-killer gun and hurry over to the spot where you'd last seen the executive and the large, powerful zombie. You search the area, but there is no sign of him.

You shake your head – there's no more you can do for Price. A zombie lurches at you from behind the 4x4, but you easily move out of its way.

"You look dead on your feet," you say before sending it back to the grave. You finish off the other zombies – you feel little pity for these creatures of the living dead – if you didn't get them, they'd get you!

‡ *You decide to continue your investigation without Mr Price. Go to 22.*

78

You go to reload you zombie-killer gun as Price lunges at you. Instinctively you roll to one side, just avoiding the virus-contaminated oil. Price swipes at you with a massive fist and you duck out of the way, but your gun clatters to the floor. Price charges towards you and knocks you to the floor, blocking the door.

01:00

You roll again, dodging his clumsy but powerful moves. Then you kick out at him, but your martial arts skills seem to have no effect on him. He grabs your leg and spins you into a wall.

00:30

78: The doorway is blocked – time is running out!

"Is that all you've got?" Price asks.

You struggle to you feet, gasping for breath.

"Tell me, Price. Where did they dig you up from?" you say, glancing over to the timer on the explosive charge.

"Huh?" He follows your stare to the wall beside him. "No!" Price screams, trying to tear the explosives off.

The only regret you have is that you won't be able to keep your promise to Manu as the ball of flame fills the room and engulfs the barrels of oil – creating an explosion you never live to see.

‡ *You have stopped Price, but you have paid with your life. If you wish to start again, go back to 1.*

79

You try a cabin door and to your relief, it opens. You duck inside, leaving it slightly open to see who or what is coming your way.

The footsteps get louder. Your finger hovers over the trigger of your gun as you wait. The figures pass by and you are surprised to see Romero Price walking in front of three zombies, who are holding guns.

- ‡ *If you want to follow the zombies and Price, go to 21.*
- ‡ *If you would prefer to leap out and attack them, go to 4.*

80

As the 4x4 skids to a halt, you unclip your zombie-killer gun from your belt.

The driver opens his window. "What's the—?" But before he can finish, a zombie thrusts its head through the window and plunges its teeth into the driver's neck. Blood spurts everywhere, covering you and Mr Price in a red spray.

As the zombie turns on you, you put your gun against the creature's head and blast its brains out. It slumps against the door.

"It's a zombie ambush!" you shout at Price as

the other zombies beat at the 4x4 with their fists, smashing the windows and reaching in towards you with their grasping hands.

- *If you want to try and escape from the jeep, go to 71.*
- *If you want to try and drive away from the ambush, go to 63.*
- *If you want to fight the zombies from inside the car, go to 34.*

81

You grab hold of a bucket and bale water from the cockpit while Manu struggles with the wheel, steering the boat through the raging waves. Rain crashes down on your body like blows from a hammer.

Then as suddenly as the storm started, it blows out and the waves gradually settle. The sun breaks through as Manu puts the boat back on course, but just as you check your weapon bag you hear a distant hum.

You look up. Off to starboard you can see three speedboats leaping across the water. The roar of powerful engines becomes louder.

"Friends of yours?" you ask Manu.

"I'm not sure I want to find out," he replies.

You quickly pick up a pair of binoculars and curse –

you can hardly believe your eyes. The boats are full of zombies! And some of them have guns. They open fire on you – shots whizzing in the air as the zombie boats close in on Manu's fishing boat.

‡ *If you want to try to outrun them, go to 18.*
‡ *If you want to prepare to fight them, go to 74.*

82

You keep hold of your gun. "I can get us out of here," you tell Price.

To your amazement, Price begins to laugh. "Ha, ha, ha. What makes you think that I want to get out of here?" he says. "Haven't you guessed yet who is behind all of this?" He points to the barrels. "Who do you think is behind the processing of all this Kaluta oil? Who arranged for you to come here? Who organised my supposed kidnap?"

Realisation suddenly hits you. "It's you!" you gasp. "You're the master of the zombies!"

"Well done, Hunter – I'm surprised you hadn't guessed earlier!"

Questions flash through your mind. How does Price control the zombies – why aren't they attacking him? You remember what the hotel receptionist told you and you eye up the hundreds of barrels stacked in

82

the hold. You think about what would happen if the zombies became covered in Kaluta oil.

Price points at you. "Now, put down your gun..."

‡ *If you want to do as he says, go to 53.*
‡ *If you want to keep Price talking, go to 12.*
‡ *If you want to try and escape, go to 40.*

83

You feel the infected blood travelling through your body, numbing your veins. You reach into your bag and take out a rope and a knife.

Looping the rope around your thigh, you pull it as tightly as you can. The sweat drips from your brow and you breathe hard as you take the knife and with all your might cut at your flesh above the knee.

The pain is excruciating and you cry out as you saw through the flesh. However, you are unable to cut through your thighbone.

Knowing there is only one thing to do, you take your gun, load it with a dumdum bullet, place it against your leg and pull the trigger. The bullet explodes, shattering your bone and sending your flesh flying. You pass out with the pain.

‡ *Go to 32.*

84

As the zombies advance you launch a rocket. There is a violent explosion and several of the zombies are blasted to pieces. You reload, but the remaining creatures scatter and break into a run. You hadn't expected this!

    ‡ *If you want to continue using the rocket launcher, go to 31.*
    ‡ *If you want to use your gun, go to 51.*

85

"We have to go back!" you shout as the storm rages around you.

"We must go on," Manu bellows back. "My family are not safe on Saruba, you can help them."

"We go back," you insist. At that moment a wave crashes across the deck, hitting you in the chest and knocking you over the side...

You plunge beneath the waves. You try to swim back towards the boat, but the sea is too rough. You disappear under the waves again... You struggle against the elements but your lungs are soon at bursting point and you pass into blackness.

    ‡ *Go to 2.*

86

You press your gun to the pilot's ear and pull the trigger. The zombie's head explodes, splattering the inside of the cockpit with brains, blood and maggots. The creature slumps forward against the controls, sending the helicopter into an even steeper dive.

Quickly, you jump over the seat, push the dead zombie aside and grab hold of the stick control that steers the helicopter. With a superhuman effort, you pull back. The helicopter responds and pulls up and away, clipping the tops of trees and narrowly avoiding a rocky hillside.

You breathe a sigh of relief and after wiping the remains of the zombie's innards from the windscreen, level off the helicopter and decide where to head.

‡ *If you wish to return to the airport, go to 38.*
‡ *If you wish to fly to Nutco's HQ in the hills, go to 19.*

87

You put the oil down on the floor and, holding your gun, unlock the door and turn the handle.

WHUMP!

You are thrown backwards as the zombie punches through the door. You lie dazed on the floor as the zombies tear down the door and move towards you.

One of them grabs your leg, nearly ripping it out of its hip joint socket. Despite the agonising pain, you manage to bring up your gun and shoot it in the head. Its brains splatter out and it drops to the floor. More zombies appear at the door. You know you are too badly injured to fight them. The only thing you can do now is try to escape.

‡ *If you wish to try and escape through the door, go to 24.*

‡ *If you want to try and escape through the window, go to 7.*

88

You turn back and hurry along the corridor. The footsteps are still heading your way. Frantically, you try the cabin doors along the corridor. Luckily one opens. You move inside, leaving it slightly open to see who or what is coming your way.

You are surprised to see Romero Price being led along the corridor by three zombies who are all holding machine guns.

⚊ *If you want to follow the zombies and Price, go to 21.*
⚊ *If you would prefer to leap out and attack them, go to 4.*

89

You shoot at the zombies, but in the confusion and growing darkness, your aim is not perfect. Parts of their undead bodies fly off in all directions, but you only hit one of the creatures in the head, blowing its brains out.

Price is still struggling with his captors as the other zombies turn their attention to you.

They head towards you, arms out, their ugly faces set in wild, groaning smiles. You aim carefully and pull the trigger. There is a metallic click – you've run out of ammunition! Cursing, you reach to your belt for another clip of bullets, but there isn't time to reload – a zombie grabs hold of you and throws you to the ground. You struggle to your knees but realise that you are badly outnumbered.

- *If you decide to leave Price to his fate, go to 15.*
- *If you wish to use your martial arts skills, go to 59.*
- *If you want to reach for your flame gun, go to 47.*

90

"Had to be sure," you say.

"The car is parked outside. I'll carry your bag." He reaches out, offering his hand.

"I'll do that." You head towards the door. Suddenly you feel a blow to your head and you crash to the floor.

You lie half-conscious, unable to move. Eric has your arms pinned behind your back. He leans close to you. His stinking breath makes you gag – zombie breath. "Coloured water in the bottle," Eric boasts before licking your ear. "You'll make a tasty breakfast," the zombie says, before sinking its teeth into your neck and ripping your soft flesh. You scream in pain and pass out.

‡   *Go to 97.*

91

You spin on the ground and sweep at the zombie's feet. It crashes to the floor. You leap up and land a kick to the zombie's rotting head – your boot goes right through its spongy skull! Maggots and pus squirt out onto the ground.

You breathe a sigh of relief.

‡   *Go to 65.*

90
91

92

With Mr Price in the next room you quickly take out
your computer phone. You access the database stored
back at your house and type in "Kaluta". Soon you
have the information you wanted.

> KALUTA OIL
The islanders on Saruba live
in fear that the dead can be
animated by evil spirits and
walk abroad. The islanders
ritually purify the graves of
their ancestors with oil from the
Kaluta nut, which grows only in
the island group around Saruba.
They claim that the oil of the
nut protects them from the undead
and can stop attacks from such
creatures...■

You tuck the phone back into your pocket just as Mr
Price returns.

"Powerful stuff, this oil," you say to Price. You
wonder why Nutco are interested in a product whose
only use seems to be in repelling zombie attacks.

‡   *Go to 5.*

93

You speed off towards the quay where the ship is docked. The noise of the large motorbike engine breaks through the clammy mist. You pull up just before the quayside. Some way ahead, you can make out a group of zombies armed with weapons and clubs. Behind them, you see a service gangway, leading onto the ship. The zombies begin to move towards you...

‡ *If you want to fire a rocket, then drive the bike onto the ship, go to 16.*

‡ *If you want to fire a rocket, then fight the zombies on foot, go to 60.*

94

"Just a second," you call out as you move quickly from your bed and pick up your gun. You tiptoe towards the door, gun held out. You reach for the handle...

CRUNCH!

The door is suddenly flung open, smashing you in the face. Stunned, you look up to see four huge figures crash into the room. Their gangrenous faces leer at you, as they reach for you with their rotting hands. You shoot at one of the zombies, hitting it in the head. Its brain splatters against the wall. You leap onto the bed, shooting at the other zombies. You kill a second, but at that moment, you are caught by a zombie's swinging blow. Your gun flies from your hand and you stumble to the floor. Two more zombies appear at the doorway.

- *If you want to try and escape through the door, go to 40.*
- *If you want to try and escape through the window, go to 7.*
- *If you want to try and grab a weapon, go to 24.*
- *If you want to use your martial arts skills, go to 59.*

95

You ready your rocket launcher and steer the fishing boat into the port. Mist begins to form around you as the still night air begins to cool. You pull up by the quayside. The port is silent except for the thrumming sound of the *Golgotha*'s engine. She must be preparing to leave.

You jump off the boat, but your arrival has been noticed. A group of zombies step out of the blanket of mist – they have been waiting for you! As they lurch towards you, their decomposing mouths groaning and snarling, you can see they are carrying guns and clubs.

‡ *If you want to tell them to take you to Price, go to 68.*
‡ *If you want to use the rocket launcher, go to 84.*
‡ *If you want to use your gun, go to 51.*

96

You try to fight back, but your situation becomes hopeless as more of the zombies take a deadly grip on you. The smell of death and rotting flesh fills the air. Their hands pull on your limbs, snapping your bones. You scream in agony as their teeth rip into your flesh and you feel yourself being torn apart. The zombies' blood mixes with yours – you feel its evil presence flooding through your veins.

Your final living thought is one of horror – you know that you are turning into a creature of the undead – destined to walk the earth as a zombie, enslaved by your craving for human flesh.

> *You have failed. If you wish to begin again, go to 1.*

97

Sometime later you wake and look up. Standing above you is a group of zombies – they stand leering at you.

You sit up and stare at your body. Your left arm is hanging on by its sinews, your legs are ripped open and black liquid oozes from the wounds.

You feel your face and pull off a large piece of skin and muscle. You look at it before putting it into your mouth and chewing at it – the taste of flesh is good!

You have become that which you wanted to destroy – a zombie!

　　　‡　*If you are brave enough to begin your adventure again, go to 1.*

98

You drive the 4x4 around the streets and by the time you find a hotel you are the only person around. It is the only place you have seen so far with lights on inside. As you pull into the car park you notice that a thin sea mist is drifting in from the bay. You park up and carry your bags to the front doors. Somewhere in the gloom a foghorn sounds its warning. You try the doors, but to your surprise they are locked. Through the glass door you can see a woman sitting at the reception desk inside, so you tap gently on the window. She frowns, then presses a button on the desk which unlocks the door remotely. You open the door and walk into the reception hallway over towards the woman – she looks surprised to see a guest.

"Can I help?" she asks: but even as she asks the question, she grabs hold of a bottle of brown liquid that rests on the desk.

"I'd like a room for tonight, please," you reply. "Do you have one?"

Instead of answering, she flicks some of the liquid at you. It lands on your face. She leans backwards and looks at you as if waiting for something to happen. You wipe the liquid from your face.

You give her a quizzical look. "What was that for, what are you doing?"

"Just checking," she replies, mysteriously. "Yes, we have a room."

‡ *If you want to go to the room immediately, go to 69.*

‡ *If you want to talk to the woman, go to 36.*

99

"OK, Eric," you smile.

Eric smiles back and gets up.

In the blink of an eye, you reach down to your weapons belt and grab your gun. You point it at Eric's head. "There seems to be a little misunderstanding – I'm waiting for someone called Manu."

"Eric" suddenly leaps at you. You were ready for this...

‡ *If you want to use you martial arts skills, go to 28.*
‡ *If you want to shoot the zombie, go to 42.*

100

"Got to go," you say as you step through the door and lock it tightly behind you.

01:00

You sprint through the corridors and up the stairs towards the deck of the ship. You know you haven't got much time.

00:30

You reach the deck and race through the mist to the railing at the edge, but you hardly have time to think as you dive from the ship into the black sea below.

00:10

There is a glowing fireball that reaches far up into the sky and you stay underneath the water to avoid being incinerated. The shock wave of the explosion ripples through the water.

When you surface, the *Golgotha* is in flames, which light up the night sky. The crackle of fire erupts from the wreck of the cargo ship and a black cloud of oil hangs in the sky. The wind blows the smoke across Saruba. You can see the remaining zombies on the quay slowly fall apart; arms dropping off and heads rolling into the water as they are covered in the droplets of Kaluta oil. You realise that soon all of the zombies will be wiped out as wind will carry the Kaluta smoke across the whole island, reducing the surviving zombies to ooze and bone.

Slowly, you swim to the shore and pull yourself up a quayside ladder and out of the water. You know you still have to keep your promise to Manu, and you head into the town to try to find his family.

This time you have beaten the forces of the supernatural, but you know there will be other creatures that you will have to deal with...

About the 2Steves

‡ Steve Barlow and Steve Skidmore have been writing together for over twenty years. Known as the 2Steves, they have written over 125 books together. Visit www.the2steves.net

Steve Barlow

‡ Born: Crewe, UK
‡ Description: Tall and hairy
‡ Most horrific job: Emptying rubbish bins
‡ Most horrific pet: Igor the cannibal gerbil
‡ Favourite horror creature: Mothra – I just love the idea of a gigantic moth that destroys whole cities!
‡ Favourite horror film: *An American Werewolf in London*

Steve Skidmore

‡ Born: Leicester, UK
‡ Description: Short and less hairy than Barlow
‡ Most horrific job: Counting pastry pie lids
‡ Most horrific pet: A mad rabbit
‡ Favourite horror creature: Vampire
   ‡ Favourite horror film: *The Omen*

Steve Barlow

iHorror: the story so far...

We came up with the idea for iHorror after writing iHero, a series of interactive books for Franklin Watts, a children's publisher. The series featured books where the reader becomes the hero, such as a gladiator or a spy or an astronaut, and decides what happens in the adventure. With iHorror, we wanted to do something much scarier!

That's right. Because we love scary stuff! And we don't think people should be laughing at zombies because they're in a daft comedy movie. Zombies really aren't very nice creatures, and iHorror is designed for people who'd rather kill the lumbering corpses than chuckle at them!

So iHorror was born. But these aren't ordinary books – which you'll already know if you've read one of the iHero titles. They are also more difficult to write than "normal" books – we have to do research, planning, more planning, writing, drawing spider diagrams to link all the paragraphs up, more writing, and then the editing starts.

And that's when the reader takes over and decides how the story will work out!

Steve Skidmore

Creating the artwork of iHorror

The inside artwork for iHorror is drawn by Paul Davidson. We've put together some pieces to show you the stages of progression. Below is the scene from paragraph 30, when the zombie assassins in the corridor are hit by Kaluta oil.

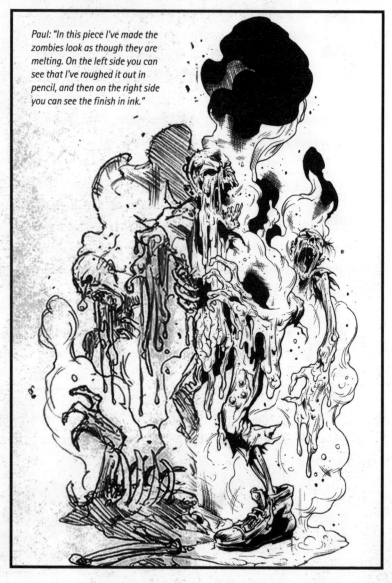

Paul: "In this piece I've made the zombies look as though they are melting. On the left side you can see that I've roughed it out in pencil, and then on the right side you can see the finish in ink."

"Rough sketch for paragraph 100 (right); inset above shows the final version used in the book."

"Rough sketch for paragraph 16 (below). The inset below right shows the final version used in the book."

"I gave the option of using different weapons in the same pose (right) – this isn't included in the competition – see the last page for details."

CROSSBOW?

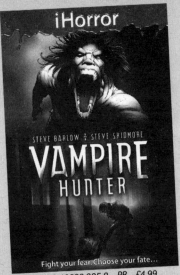

iHorror

STEVE BARLOW ÷ STEVE SKIDMORE

VAMPIRE
HUNTER

Fight your fear. Choose your fate...

978 1 40830 985 8   PB   £4.99

iHorror: Vampire Hunter
Sneak peek

It is a cold, dark January evening and you have received news that a vampire has arrived in London, seeking new blood for the new year. Using your expertise in hunting down supernatural creatures, you have tracked the vampire across the city to its lair – an old, abandoned London tube train station. Armed with a flamer that shoots jets of fire and a gun that fires wooden bullets for shooting vampires through their undead hearts, you make your way to your date with the vampire.

Go to 1.

1

It is dusk and snow is falling as you arrive at the underground station in your SUV. You step out of your vehicle and shiver – not with cold but at the thought of what you will have to face in the coming hours. Above you, the outline of a full moon hangs in the darkening sky. "Just right for vampire hunting," you mutter to yourself. Your feet crunch on the recently fallen snow as you make your way to the metal shuttered door of the station. To your surprise it is open – perhaps someone, or rather something, is expecting you...

You step inside the abandoned station. It is pitch black so you activate your night-vision goggles. The goggles cut through the dark and you see several fat rats running around. But you're here for pest control of the undead kind. You move across the ticket hall and see two signs pointing to different sets of stairs.

One reads, "To the service tunnel" and the other, "To the platform".

‡ *To go down the service tunnel stairway, go to 49.*
‡ *To head towards the platform, go to 90.*
‡ *To investigate the ticket hall, go to 32.*

TO BE CONTINUED IN
        iHORROR: VAMPIRE HUNTER...

iHorror

STEVE BARLOW ‡ STEVE SKIDMORE

WEREWOLF HUNTER

Fight your fear. Choose your fate...

978 1 40830 987 2   PB   £4.99

A full moon hangs high in the sky, casting an evil glow. Werewolves are on the prowl for flesh, gathering in numbers and strength. You must track these inhuman creatures across North America to fight face-to-face with the pack leader before time runs out and the Great Hunt begins. Go now! Stop the rampage of the werewolves in its tracks.

The Japanese island of Okinawa is rocked by a massive earthquake – opening a fiery portal to the underworld! Terrible demons flood through, bent on tormenting humankind and making Earth a living nightmare. Only you can stand up to these unearthly horrors. Only you can send them back to the depths where they belong.

iHorror

STEVE BARLOW ‡ STEVE SKIDMORE

DEMON HUNTER

Fight your fear. Choose your fate...

978 1 40830 988 9   PB   £4.99

iHorror

Win a Nintendo DS Lite!*

The hunt is on...

Prove your skill as a hunter by locating the
Hunter silhouettes lurking in the pages of the
iHorror books (your first one is at the bottom
of this page). Once you have found them in ALL
FOUR iHorror titles, write the TOTAL number of
silhouettes on a postcard with your name, age
and address, and send it to:

iHorror Hunter Competition
Orchard Books Marketing Department
338 Euston Road
London NW1 3BH

Or email your answer and details to:
competitions@hachettechildrens.co.uk

Competition closes 31 August 2011.

For full terms and conditions visit:
www.orchardbooks.co.uk

Fight your fear. Choose your fate.

*This competition will run across all four iHorror books published
in 2011. There will be one prize draw. Only one entry per child.

I. Horror

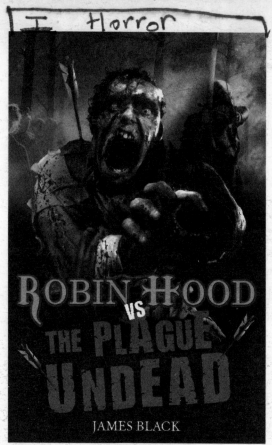

ROBIN HOOD VS THE PLAGUE UNDEAD

JAMES BLACK

9781408313886 PB £5.99

*His lungs were gone. He was completely hollow inside.
But he was not dead. Not quite.*

What happens when Robin Hood and his Merry Men are
faced with a plague of zombies? Somehow, Robin must
figure out a way to defeat the most difficult and
dangerous enemy he's ever faced, and save the
country from destruction...

ORCHARD BOOKS
www.orchardbooks.co.uk